# Sweet Valley High

## *Secrets*

Written by
## KATE WILLIAM

Created by
## FRANCINE PASCAL

### Level 2

Retold by Annette Barnes
Series Editors: Andy Hopkins and Jocelyn Potter

**Pearson Education Limited**
Edinburgh Gate, Harlow,
Essex CM20 2JE, England
and Associated Companies throughout the world.

ISBN 0 582 41768 6

First published in Great Britain by Transworld Publishers Ltd 1984
This adaptation first published by Penguin Books 1998
Published by Addison Wesley Longman Limited and Penguin Books Ltd. 1998
New edition first published 1999

Original copyright © Francine Pascal 1983
Text copyright © Annette Barnes 1998
Illustrations copyright © Bob Harvey 1998
Sweet Valley High TV © 1994, 1995 Saban
Cover photo TM and © 1994 Saban
All rights reserved

Typeset by Digital Type, London
Set in 11/14pt Bembo
Printed in Spain by Mateu Cromo, S. A. Pinto (Madrid)

Published by Pearson Education Limited in association with
Penguin Books Ltd, both companies being subsidiaries of Pearson Plc

For a complete list of the titles available in the Penguin Readers series please write to your local
Pearson Education office or to: Marketing Department, Penguin Longman Publishing,
5 Bentinck Street, London W1M 5RN.

# Contents

# Introduction

*Jessica wanted to be dance queen more than anything in the world and when she wanted something, she usually got it. But Bruce Patman was more difficult. Jessica was in love with Bruce but he never smiled at her or spoke to her. He was good-looking and rich and he was the only boy for her. But he didn't want Jessica.*

In Sweet Valley High School everybody knows Jessica Wakefield wants to be queen at the autumn dance in school. The dance is very important in the school year. Two of the students are king and queen of the dance and it is a big night for them. This year only one person can stop Jessica – Enid Rollins. Then one day Jessica finds that Enid has a secret. Jessica thinks she can use this to help her – and she will play dirty to get what she wants. But there is a problem with her plan; Enid's best friend is Elizabeth, Jessica's twin sister.

Francine Pascal wrote the first *Sweet Valley High* book in 1982 and suddenly thousands of 12-16-year-olds wanted to know more about Jessica, Elizabeth and their friends. Now Francine Pascal plans the stories but six other writers write the books. Because a lot of young people want to read these stories there are now three new books every month. You can buy over 150 different *Sweet Valley High* books. *Sweet Valley High* came to Great Britain in 1984. Now there are over 50,000 books sold every month in the UK. You can buy the books in 22 countries (Russia and Indonesia are two of them) and in 15 languages. In the USA and the UK you can watch *Sweet Valley High* on television now and soon other countries will see it too.

# Who's Who in Sweet Valley High

Jessica Wakefield ↔ Elizabeth Wakefield
(sisters)

The boy
she wants:
Bruce Patman

Her **boyfriend:**
Todd Wilkins

Her friend:
Enid Rollins

Her friends:
Cara Walker

Enid's boyfriend:
Ronnie Edwards

Lila Fowler

Enid's old friend:
George Warren

**Other students:**

Ken Matthews

Winston Egbert

**Teachers at Sweet Valley High:**

Mr Collins      Ms Nora Dalton

## Chapter 1   Enid's Secret

It was September, the beginning of the new school year, and in Sweet Valley High the students were all excited. They talked about only one thing. It was two weeks before the autumn dance at the school and for everybody this was a very important date.

'Everybody knows Bruce Patman is going to be king of the dance,' said Jessica Wakefield to her friend, Cara Walker. They were in Cara's bedroom one day after school.

'And you're going to be queen,' said Cara. 'I know you'll win. You're much prettier than all the other girls at school.' Cara was right. Jessica was very pretty, with long hair the colour of the sun and beautiful blue-green eyes.

'Enid Rollins can win – she's very pretty and Ronnie Edwards is her boyfriend,' said Jessica. 'He's planning the king and queen competition this year so he can help Enid win.'

After the competition every year the dance king and queen went together to all school dances for the rest of the year. Jessica wanted to be dance queen more than anything in the world and when she wanted something, she usually got it. But Bruce Patman was more difficult. Jessica was in love with Bruce but he never smiled at her or spoke to her. He was good-looking and rich and he was the only boy for her. But he didn't want Jessica.

'When we're king and queen it will be different,' she thought. 'He's going to fall in love with me at the dance.'

She thought about his blue eyes and dark hair, and his beautiful black Porsche. He drove it to school every day and she thought about sitting next to him in that car every morning and evening.

'Enid mustn't win, Cara,' she said. 'This is much more important for me than for her and I *must* win.'

◆

1

Jessica's twin sister, Elizabeth, was at home that evening with her best friend, Enid Rollins. The twins had the same hair, the same eyes and the same pretty faces but they were very different girls. Elizabeth was quieter than Jessica and they didn't always like doing the same things. Sometimes they went out together but often they each went with their different friends.

That evening Enid was unhappy and Elizabeth couldn't understand why. They sat in the kitchen with a cup of coffee and Elizabeth asked her friend, 'Why are you so sad? What's the problem, Enid?' But Enid didn't want to tell her and she started crying.

'Please tell me what's wrong, perhaps I can help,' said Elizabeth.

'You can't help, Liz. Nobody can. I'm afraid I'm going to lose Ronnie,' Enid said. 'He won't want me for his girl any more. Not when he knows about me.'

Elizabeth didn't understand.

'When he knows what? What is this bad secret you're afraid of?'

They went up to Elizabeth's room and Enid took some papers out of her bag. She gave them to Elizabeth.

'These are letters from a boy called George. We're only friends but Ronnie won't understand that. He's very jealous,' she said. 'I never see George now, but I wrote to him soon after he went away. I think my letters helped him in the beginning. Now we usually write every week.'

'When did you meet him?' asked Elizabeth.

'Two years ago I had a difficult time at home and I was very unhappy. I started going out with George and some of his friends and one afternoon he took his father's car. It was very dangerous because he drove it much too fast. We had an accident and the police came. After that, George's mother and father sent him to a school in another town and I came to Sweet Valley High.'

'But you write to him now?'

'These are letters from a boy called George.'

'He's different now and I am, too. He was very unhappy after the accident happened and I wanted to help him. I only write as a friend, Liz, but I can't tell Ronnie.'

Elizabeth was very sorry for Enid.

'Talk to Ronnie, tell him everything and he'll understand. He loves you.'

But Enid knew it wasn't as easy as that.

'It's worse than you think, Liz. In his last letter George says he wants to see me when he comes home next time. I don't know what to do. I don't want to stop being George's friend but Ronnie will kill him. And I don't want to lose Ronnie.'

They sat together on Elizabeth's bed and thought about the problem.

'Only you and I know about the letters, Enid. And I'm not going to tell Ronnie – I'm your best friend, remember? Everything's going to be OK, you'll see.'

Enid stayed the night at Elizabeth's house and in the morning she put the letters back in her bag with all her other things. But she didn't see one of George's letters fall to the floor and go under Elizabeth's bed.

♦

Jessica sat in her French lesson and thought about Bruce Patman. Next to her was Winston Egbert and all he could think about was Jessica. Winston wasn't good-looking or rich and so Jessica didn't like him. But Winston was a nice boy and he was friends with most of the Sweet Valley High students. He knew Jessica didn't want him as her boyfriend and he knew she was in love with Bruce. Everybody knew that.

Jessica thought about the autumn dance. She wanted to go to the dance with Bruce and she wanted to win the competition. It was the most important thing to her.

'Then he'll fall in love with me,' she said quietly.

Some of the students in front of Jessica heard her. They turned round and looked at her.

'She's talking about me,' said Winston, and laughed. Jessica turned away and looked out of the window.

Their French teacher, Nora Dalton, waited for the other students to stop laughing.

'OK, let's get back to some work,' she said.

Ms Dalton was young and very pretty. Most of the students liked her a lot but one or two of the girls were jealous of her. Sometimes they said things about her, but they weren't true. Stories about people in school went round Sweet Valley High very quickly. There was a story at that time about Ms Dalton and Ken Matthews, one of her students. The story was that he was her boyfriend, but it wasn't true.

After the French lesson Jessica talked to Cara.

'How can I stop Enid winning?' she asked.

'She won't win. She isn't as pretty as you, Jess.'

'But what about Ronnie? Don't forget he's her boyfriend. Everybody says he loves her very much, but why? I don't understand it!' she said.

Jessica didn't like Enid and it wasn't only because of the dance- queen competition. She was jealous because Elizabeth was often with her and they were very good friends. Before they met, Elizabeth went out with Jessica more.

Suddenly Jessica saw Bruce turn a corner and walk out of the school building.

'He's one in a million,' she thought.

She forgot about Enid and Ronnie and stopped walking with Cara.

'I must go, Cara. See you later,' she said and quickly ran after Bruce.

'Hi, Bruce,' she said and smiled as beautifully as she could. She started walking next to him.

'Smile that beautiful smile for him and I know he'll ask you.'

'Hi, Jessica,' he said, 'you're not usually alone. Where are the other girls today?'

'I don't always want to be with the girls. I'm often alone, Bruce. I haven't got anyone to go to the dance with and it's only another two weeks.'

Bruce stopped walking. He looked at her and smiled. Jessica waited for him to ask her. But then he said, 'I think Winston will take you. Why don't you ask him?'

Jessica laughed. 'Winston Egbert? I don't want to go with Winston! He can't dance – and *look* at him, Bruce. Oh no, I can't go to the dance with him,' she said.

'OK, but think about it. You don't want to go to the dance alone,' said Bruce, and then he laughed. 'Here comes Winston now. Smile that beautiful smile for him and I know he'll ask you. See you later, Jessica,' he said, and then he walked away.

'Hi, Jess,' said Winston, with his face going red. 'Do you want to walk with me to the next lesson?'

'No thanks, Winston. I must see Liz first and I'm late now.' She looked at Bruce's back but he didn't look round at her. Then she turned and ran into school.

## Chapter 2   Jessica Starts the Plan

When Jessica got home from school that day she wasn't very happy. Bruce said her smile was beautiful, but then, when she thought he was interested in her, he suddenly left her with Winston.

Jessica's mother was in the kitchen. She said hello to her daughter and started washing the vegetables for dinner.

'Where's Liz?' Jessica asked her.

'I think she's with Enid,' Alice Wakefield said. 'They're doing something together at Enid's house for the school dance.'

'Enid! How can Liz want to be with her so often? I don't understand it,' said Jessica.

'Enid's a very nice girl, Jess, and Liz likes her a lot. I think you're a little jealous,' Alice said to Jessica.

'Me? Jealous of Enid Rollins? Why?'

'Because Liz goes out with Enid a lot and you don't see her as much now.'

'Liz can see anybody she wants,' said Jessica. 'Don't forget I brought Enid home first.'

Alice Wakefield knew the problem. Enid liked Elizabeth better than she liked Jessica. But she didn't say any more and soon Jessica went up to her room.

She started doing some school work but then she remembered she wanted to use a book. She knew that book was in Elizabeth's bedroom.

She went into Elizabeth's room and sat on her bed. She started thinking about the dance again. Elizabeth had her boyfriend, Todd Wilkins. Enid had Ronnie Edwards. A lot of boys wanted to take Jessica to the dance but she only wanted Bruce. And Bruce didn't want her.

Her plan to be dance queen was good, but because Ronnie

*'Me? Jealous of Enid Rollins? Why?'*

loved Enid, he wanted her to win. He could get a lot of students to vote for her. Jessica couldn't think of an answer to the problem. She was quite unhappy and she started crying.

Then she saw something under Elizabeth's bed. When she pulled it out, she saw it was a letter and she started reading.

'"Dear Enid",' she read. ' "Thanks for your last letter. Your letters are a big help to me. I'm OK but I can't stop thinking about the bad things we did . . ."'

Jessica stopped crying and started smiling. Suddenly she had another plan.

◆

The next evening Elizabeth and Todd went to the cinema with Enid and Ronnie. Usually they had a good time together but that evening something was different.

'Ronnie is very quiet,' said Todd. 'Perhaps they had a fight before we came here.'

Elizabeth was very worried about Enid. She hadn't told Todd or anybody about Enid and George's letters but she started to think that perhaps Ronnie knew Enid's secret.

When the film finished, Enid and Elizabeth walked out together and there was time to talk.

'What's wrong with Ronnie?' asked Elizabeth.

'I don't know,' said Enid. 'He's very different tonight – a million miles away. Oh, Liz, do you think he knows?'

'How can he know?' said Elizabeth. 'Perhaps it's something different – a family problem or something at school.'

'It's not easy for him – he lives alone with his father after his mother left home.'

'Perhaps that's the problem – he had a fight with his father before he came out,' said Elizabeth. 'You must talk to him Enid.'

'I'll try,' said Enid. 'But it won't be easy.'

Ronnie drove Todd and Elizabeth home. Then before they got

*Then she saw something under Elizabeth's bed.*

to Enid's house he turned the car off the road and stopped. It was a quiet place. They looked down to the town below.

Enid knew something was wrong. Ronnie kissed her but it wasn't the same.

'Ronnie, what's the problem – what's wrong?' she asked him.

'I didn't want to tell you . . . but it's about the dance. I can't go because my dad wants me to help him in the shop that night.'

Ronnie's father had an all-night supermarket in the town but Enid knew he didn't have to ask Ronnie to help. Other people sometimes helped Mr Edwards in the shop.

'I'm sorry we can't go together. I don't want to go alone,' she said.

Ronnie put his arm round her again and kissed her. But his kiss was hard and something told her it was all wrong. She pulled away from him.

'Can't we sit and talk?'

'What about?' said Ronnie. 'You and George?'

'How . . . how do you know about George?'

'That isn't important. I know a lot of things about you now. About the car and the police . . .'

Enid put her hands over her eyes. She didn't want to look at Ronnie.

'You don't understand – please listen to me Ronnie,' she said.

But Ronnie was very jealous and he didn't want to listen to anything.

'Oh, I understand, Enid. All the time I thought you were in love with me, you had another boyfriend. You wrote him love letters!'

'That isn't true! George and I are only friends. I last saw him a long time ago – more than two years. He isn't a boyfriend . . .'

Ronnie said nothing and then Enid started getting angry. 'OK, Ronnie. You can think anything you want to!'

He started the car.

'How . . . how do you know about George?'

'I'll take you home, then it's over between us,' he said.

They drove to Enid's house without a word and she tried not to cry. All the time there was one thought in her head: *Liz told him about the letters!*

♦

Jessica was happy. She went into Elizabeth's room and showed her two dresses, one blue and one green.

'Which is best? Which dress shall I wear tonight? What do you think, Liz?'

Elizabeth didn't understand. Why did Jessica want to look nice for a Saturday night out with Cara?

'I don't know. They're the same to me,' she said.

'Don't you want to know about tonight? Ask me where we're going!' said Jessica.

'No, I'm not interested.'

Jessica wasn't happy with that.

'OK, I'll tell you. Lila's having a party,' she said. Lila wasn't one of Elizabeth's friends. Her family were very rich and had a big house in town.

'Have a good time,' said Elizabeth and started reading her book again.

'Everybody will be there – everybody important.'

Elizabeth started to understand. 'Bruce Patman?' she asked.

'Yes, Bruce is going so I must look good. Now, which dress? I think the blue.' She walked out of Elizabeth's room and went back to her room.

Elizabeth stopped reading. She was worried about Enid. They went to the cinema on Friday and now it was Saturday evening.

'Why didn't she phone me today?' thought Elizabeth. 'She knows I'm worried about her and Ronnie. Perhaps she talked to Ronnie and the problem got worse. And now she's angry with me because it was my plan . . .'

'Everybody will be there – everybody important.'

Elizabeth called Enid's house and her mother answered.

'She can't come to the phone – sorry, but she's got a lot of things to do,' she said.

Ten minutes later Elizabeth tried again. This time Enid answered but she wasn't as friendly as she usually was.

'Are you OK, Enid?'

'No, I'm not. Ronnie and I are finished. He knows about the letters.'

'How can he know? Only you and I knew about them!' said Elizabeth.

'That's right,' said Enid.

'Oh Enid, you can't think I told him . . .'

'I know I didn't tell him. Only one other person saw the letters – you. I thought you were my friend, Liz. Oh, why did you do this to me?'

'Enid, please . . .'

But before she finished, Enid put the phone down. Elizabeth sat and looked at the phone.

'Who was that?' Jessica asked from behind her.

'It was Enid – she and Ronnie are finished and she thinks it's because of me.'

Elizabeth told Jessica the story.

'There was a mistake, Liz. Perhaps she told somebody about the letters before you and now she can't remember it. You're better without her,' said Jessica, and she put her arms round her sister.

'I think it's a good thing Ronnie knows about the letters.'

'But who was it? Who?' asked Elizabeth.

Jessica didn't answer her. It was late and she didn't want to talk to Elizabeth about Enid's problems. She wanted to go to the party and talk to Bruce.

# Chapter 3   The Story Goes Round the School

Lila Fowler lived in the best street in town. Her mother died when she was a little girl and now her father was friendly with Nora Dalton, her French teacher. He often took her to dinner or to the cinema. Lila was jealous and she didn't like Ms Dalton because of this. She started the story about Nora and Ken Matthews but she knew it wasn't true. She thought Nora was only interested in her father because of his money. He was very rich and they had a beautiful house and garden.

When Jessica arrived at the house she looked first for Bruce. A lot of Sweet Valley High students were there before her but she couldn't see Bruce.

'I hear Ronnie and Enid are finished,' Cara said to Jessica. 'Why don't you go and talk to Ronnie? He looks quite unhappy alone there.'

'No thanks. I'm waiting for somebody more interesting,' said Jessica.

'You can forget Bruce,' said Lila. 'He's not coming tonight.'

'What?' Jessica nearly fell off her chair.

'He called and said that he's going to another party in town. Do you know, he's taking a nineteen-year-old girl to the dance! Why does someone that old want to go to a high school dance? I can't understand it,' said Lila.

Jessica's heart fell down to her shoes. 'He's taking another girl to the dance,' she thought sadly. But soo she started to think of a new plan.

Lila and Cara started talking about Ms Dalton and Ken Matthews but Jessica wasn't interested. She finished her drink and went across the room to Ronnie.

'Hi, Ronnie,' she said to him, 'why are you unhappy? This is a party – aren't you having a good time? Let's dance!'

Ronnie was angry. 'Someone told me Enid had a letter from another boy. It finished with the words, "Love from George".'

'No thanks, Jessica. Later, perhaps.'

'I can see you're sad about Enid. Don't you think she's sorry you had a fight?'

Ronnie was angry. 'I know she isn't sorry,' he said. 'Someone wrote to me yesterday. They told me Enid had a letter from another boy. It finished with the words, "Love from George". And I thought Enid was my girl.'

'Yes,' said Jessica, 'Liz said something about George. So you aren't taking Enid to the dance now?'

'No, I'm not, I'm going to stay at home that night. Every other girl is going with somebody now. It's too late, the dance is next Saturday.'

Jessica smiled her best smile.

'I'm not going with anybody,' she said. 'Why don't we go together?'

'OK Jessica, why not?' he said.

Jessica took his hand. 'Good! Now let's dance,' she said.

♦

At school on Monday morning Enid started to walk past Elizabeth without saying anything. But Elizabeth stopped her. 'Enid, we must talk,' she said.

'Why? There's nothing to talk about. And I don't want to say anything to you, Elizabeth Wakefield.'

'Enid, you're my best friend and I didn't tell anybody about those letters,' she said with her hand on her heart. 'I don't understand. What's happening? Perhaps I'll talk to Ronnie . . .'

Enid was very angry. 'Don't say anything to him! Don't say any more to anybody about us! We're finished now – thanks to you . . .'

She started crying and then turned and walked away. Elizabeth was very sad.

Cara saw Enid and Elizabeth. She listened to them and then

she watched Enid walk away. Then she told Lila, and Lila told a friend or two. Before the afternoon everybody in Sweet Valley High knew that Ronnie and Enid weren't together now and it was because of Elizabeth.

'Don't worry,' Jessica said to Elizabeth. 'It's Enid's problem, you didn't do anything wrong. I'll talk to her for you.'

'I don't know – do you think it will help?'

'Perhaps – who knows?'

Jessica found Enid near the school café.

'Liz is very unhappy about everything,' she said.

'She's unhappy? What about me? I lost my boyfriend thanks to Liz. I told her my secret and she put a knife in my back.'

'It didn't happen like that, Enid. Liz didn't want to tell Ronnie, it was an accident – a mistake. She didn't plan it.'

'Jessica, I know you're trying to help. But you can tell Liz I'll never forget this. OK?' said Enid, and she walked away.

Jessica smiled a little. 'Now Enid and Ronnie aren't together, she can't be queen,' she thought. 'So look out, Bruce Patman – here I come!'

◆

Elizabeth and Jessica were in their bedrooms that evening when the phone rang. Their mother answered it.

'Jessica,' she called, 'Ronnie Edwards is on the phone for you.'

When Jessica came back Elizabeth asked, 'Why does Ronnie want to talk to you? I didn't think you knew him very well.'

'I didn't before Saturday but he was at Lila's party and we started talking. I'm going to the dance with him,' she said and she sat down on Elizabeth's bed.

'What?' said Elizabeth, 'Enid will be very unhappy about that.'

'I think when he sees her at the dance and she sees him – perhaps everything will be OK again. Then Enid will stop being angry with you. I'm only trying to help.'

'I lost my boyfriend thanks to Liz. I told her my secret and she put a knife in my back.'

'I don't think Enid is going to the dance now. She hasn't got anybody to go with.'

'Tell her she must go,' said Jessica.

'How can I tell her? She isn't talking to me. She looked very angry when I saw her after school today. What did you say to her this afternoon?'

'Nothing much. But she said some very bad things about you, Liz,' said Jessica. 'I think she's jealous of you because you have Todd and now she hasn't got a boyfriend.'

Jessica stood up and started looking in Elizabeth's cupboard.

'Can I use your evening bag on Saturday at the dance? It will look very pretty with my red dress.'

'No, I want to use it . . .'

Jessica didn't listen.

'But you're wearing your green dress. Why don't you use Mum's bag? That will look much better with green, Liz. What do you think?'

Elizabeth didn't want a fight with Jessica so she said, 'Perhaps you're right. Oh, OK Jess. Take the bag.'

Jessica kissed her and went back to her bedroom with the evening bag. Soon Elizabeth heard her singing happily.

## Chapter 4    Elizabeth Understands

The next day Elizabeth went to see Mr Collins in his office about her problem with Enid. She liked him best of all her teachers and she knew he was interested in his students and wanted to know their problems. 'He'll help me,' she thought.

She told him about the letters and why Enid was angry with her.

'The first thing you must think about is: Why did somebody want to tell Ronnie about the letters?' Mr Collins said. 'When you know that, you can start thinking about the answer to the next question – who?'

'But that's the problem,' said Elizabeth. 'Nobody but me knew about the letters.'

Mr Collins walked around his desk and sat down next to Elizabeth.

'That's what Enid thinks,' he said. 'But it wasn't you, so one other person here knows about them. Perhaps more than one person knows. Now, we must start being detectives. What about this George? Has he got any friends in Sweet Valley High?'

Elizabeth thought for a minute.

'Enid says he was friends with Winston Egbert when they were little,' she said quietly.

'OK, so perhaps Winston knew.'

Elizabeth wasn't very happy with that.

'So, let's say Winston knew – but why tell Ronnie? They aren't friends and they don't go out with the same people.'

'Sometimes it's an accident when people tell secrets. I don't think Winston is a bad person, but you know he talks a lot!'

'Perhaps Mr Collins is right,' Elizabeth thought.

'I can ask Winston,' she said.

'Tonight's the dance and we're going to have
a very good time together,' Todd said.

Todd took her hand.

'You can't do anything more Liz.'

'But there's something wrong. Do you think somebody is telling her bad things about me?' asked Elizabeth. 'Jess says I'm better without her.'

Todd didn't like Jessica.

'Don't listen to Jessica, she's not always right. Now, try to forget about your problems with Enid. Tonight's the dance and we're going to have a very good time together,' he said and he kissed her again.

◆

When Elizabeth got home that afternoon Jessica met her at the door.

'Mum says we must clean our rooms or we can't go to the dance tonight,' she said angrily.

'That's OK, we've got hours before the dance.'

'It's OK for you – your room is always clean. My room's much worse,' said Jessica.

'I can't understand that – you're always in my room,' said Elizabeth. 'I know you like it better than your room but I never go into your room without being asked. And never when you aren't there.'

Jessica quickly went back to her room and Elizabeth started putting away some books in her bedroom. There were one or two school papers on the floor. She looked at them and then she saw the corner of another paper under her bed. She pulled it out and read the first words.

It was one of George's letters!

Elizabeth sat on her bed.

'Somebody found it here,' she thought. 'Ronnie knows because somebody found this letter and then told him . . .'

Then she thought again. Only her mother and one other

person went in her room when she wasn't there and suddenly she understood everything.

It was Jessica. Jessica found the letter and wrote to Ronnie. She told him everything. And Elizabeth understood why.

'Jessica wants to be queen and nothing or nobody is going to stop her. Not me, not Ronnie — and not Enid,' she thought angrily.

Elizabeth put the letter in her cupboard. She was very angry with Jessica and she wanted to kill her.

◆

After school Enid went to see Nora Dalton at her house. She liked her better than all the other teachers at Sweet Valley High, and sometimes she went to her for help. It was often easier for Enid to talk to Ms Dalton than to her mother.

When Nora opened the door Enid thought she was ill. Her face was white and she looked very unhappy.

They went into the sitting room and sat down together. Then Enid told her story.

'But Liz is much too nice to do that,' said Nora Dalton.

'Jessica said it was an accident — perhaps that's true. But Liz knew how important it was to me that Ronnie didn't know.'

'Does Liz say it was an accident?'

'No, she says she didn't tell Ronnie.'

'Perhaps that *is* true, Enid. Talk to her, say you're sorry and try to be friends again. Perhaps she can help you find out the answer.' Nora Dalton smiled at Enid. 'Are you going to the dance tonight?'

'No, I don't want to go alone,' said Enid sadly.

'Why not? Other students are going alone. Don't run away from your problems, Enid. Go to the dance and let people see you aren't afraid.'

*When Nora opened the door Enid thought she was ill.*

'Are you going?' Enid asked Nora.

'No ... no I don't think I want to ... it's a little difficult because ...' She stopped talking suddenly. Enid knew she was unhappy because of the story going around school about her and Ken Matthews.

'Oh Ms Dalton, everybody's saying bad things about you. I don't like it and I know it isn't true!' she said.

'I'm thinking of leaving Sweet Valley High, Enid. On Monday I'm going to talk to ...'

Enid jumped to her feet.

'No, you can't do that!' she said. 'You can't run away! You told me not to, but now *you're* running away from *your* problems!' Before Ms Dalton could say anything Enid went to the door and it closed behind her.

◆

Enid was nearly ready to go to the dance when she heard somebody at the front door. Her mother called up to her, 'Enid! Somebody's here to see you.'

Enid thought perhaps it was Ronnie and she went out of her bedroom very quickly. But when she came to the door of the living room she stopped suddenly.

'George!'

He took her hand in his.

'You look beautiful,' he said, and Enid thought, 'And you're very good-looking now!'

George looked very different, much better than she remembered. He smiled at her.

'I talked to Winston this afternoon. I'm sorry my letters gave you some problems,' he said.

Enid smiled. 'Problems? No, forget it.'

'But Winston told me about your boyfriend.'

'It's OK. I'm going to the dance alone.'

30

*George took Enid's hand in his. 'You look beautiful,' he said.*

'No, you're not,' said George. 'You're going with me!' and he put his arms round Enid and kissed her.

Suddenly, Enid forgot about Ronnie. George was the only boy for her now and she wanted to go to the dance with him.

## Chapter 5   The Autumn Dance

'Well, how do I look?'

Jessica turned round in front of her sister. She wore a long, red dress with black shoes.

Elizabeth stopped doing her hair and looked at Jessica. She was very angry but she didn't want her to know.

'I think you'll win the competition easily,' she said.

'Do you? Oh Liz, I can't wait! Me and Bruce Patman!' said Jessica.

'Don't get too excited – he's not the only boy in the competition, you know. Don't forget Winston is going to try too,' said Elizabeth. 'And I think he'll be a very good king for some lucky girl.'

Jessica didn't want to talk about Winston. She didn't understand why he was in the competition or why Elizabeth liked him. Behind her hand Elizabeth smiled a little.

'Tonight I'm going to teach you a lesson, Jessica,' she thought.

◆

Elizabeth and Jessica arrived at the dance with Todd and Ronnie at eight–thirty.

'I can't wait for the voting to start,' Jessica said. Elizabeth smiled but she didn't say anything.

Lila walked past them and said hello, then she went across the room to some other girls. Elizabeth followed Lila and said something quietly in her ear. As soon as she walked back to Todd, Lila turned and started talking to her friends and they all looked at Jessica and Ronnie.

After about half an hour Nora Dalton arrived. She wore a long black dress and her hair was beautiful with a flower behind one ear. She looked very pretty and a lot of students watched her walk across the room. Somebody called to her, 'Hey, Ms Dalton – where's Ken?' but all she did was smile and walk to the bar. Some of the other teachers were there and Mr Collins said something to her. Then he took her hand and together they went to dance.

'Where *is* Ken?' Elizabeth asked Todd.

'Didn't you hear? He asked Lila to go to the dance with him weeks ago. But yesterday he found out about her. Lila started the story about him and Ms Dalton because she was jealous of her. Ken was very angry and he finished with her. Lila came alone tonight but Ken stayed at home,' Todd told her.

Elizabeth looked around the room. She smiled when she saw Jessica talking to Bruce Patman. Then she looked at the door and saw Enid arrive with a very good-looking boy. Enid looked beautiful in a long light blue dress and everybody watched them walk into the room. Nobody knew this boy and so they were all interested.

Soon, Elizabeth saw Enid coming across the room to her. She was worried because Enid wasn't smiling at her. She thought perhaps she was angry with her again.

'This is going to be difficult,' she thought, but then Enid put her hand on Elizabeth's arm and smiled a little.

'Liz? Can we talk? I know you're angry and I understand that, but I want to say "sorry" to you.'

'*You're* sorry?' said Liz.

'Yes, I know now you didn't tell Ronnie about the letters but I was very unhappy at the time,' said Enid.

Elizabeth put her arms round her friend.

'It's OK, Enid. I know who told Ronnie, and tonight she's going to learn an important lesson. Now tell me – who's that boy with you?'

Enid told Elizabeth about George.

'When I was with Ronnie I tried hard to be somebody I wasn't. With George it's different – I can be me, because it's me he likes.

Then Enid put her hand on Elizabeth's arm and smiled a little.

George walked across to them and gave Enid and Elizabeth a drink. They talked together for some time then George and Enid went to dance. They danced very well together and a lot of people watched them. Some of the girls looked jealous of Enid. Jessica stopped talking to Bruce and watched them dance for a minute or two. Ronnie looked angry. And Ms Dalton and Mr Collins stopped dancing for a minute and said hello to them. They looked very happy for Enid.

◆

At ten o'clock Jessica ran over to her sister.

'They're starting the voting,' she said. 'I'm very excited, I can't wait!'

Elizabeth smiled at her and thought, 'And perhaps you're getting *too* excited!'

They stood together and waited. Soon Ronnie came to say the names of the king and queen.

'First our new queen,' he said. 'And the winner is . . . Jessica Wakefield!'

'No, it can't be true!' cried Jessica. She ran across the room and stood next to Ronnie. As she smiled at everybody she thought, 'It must be Bruce . . . please, please.'

'And now,' said Ronnie, 'Our new king is . . .'

Everybody waited. Jessica looked across the room at Bruce and thought, 'Please . . .'

'. . . Winston Egbert!' said Ronnie.

Jessica's heart fell. She thought, 'Now I'll never be Bruce's girl.'

Cara and Lila ran over to Jessica.

'We're so happy for you, Jess,' they said.

'Why?' said Jessica. 'Now I must go to all the school dances this year with Winston Egbert. I think I'm going to cry!'

'But we thought you wanted to be with Winston,' said Cara. 'Everybody is saying that. We all voted for him.'

'Who started that story? I'll kill her,' said Jessica, angrily. She remembered that Elizabeth said, 'Winston will be a very good king for some lucky girl.' Then she knew.

'OK, Liz. I know it was you,' she said to her, angrily. 'Everybody voted for Winston because of you. But why? I don't understand.'

'Because of what you did to Enid. You told Ronnie about George's letters because you didn't want Enid to be queen. Aren't you happy now you've got what you want, Jess?'

Jessica was quieter now.

'I won't do it. I'll say I don't want to be queen now,' she said.

'Oh yes you will, Jess,' said Elizabeth. 'Or I'll tell everybody in school about Enid's letters. I don't think you want all your friends to know you told her secret to Ronnie. It wasn't a good thing to do, Jess. So be nice to Winston and smile.'

A photographer arrived to take photos of the new king and queen together. Jessica wanted to cry but she knew she had to smile and look happy. Elizabeth said something very quietly to the photographer and then he said, 'How about a kiss for the photo?'

Winston kissed Jessica and she closed her eyes and tried to think of Bruce. But when she opened them again and saw her sister she thought, 'I'll kill you for this, Liz!'

Later, the new king and queen danced together and Jessica saw Bruce. He looked at her and smiled one of his beautiful smiles. Jessica's heart jumped and she thought, 'Perhaps he does like me after all . . . tomorrow I'll start thinking of another plan . . .'

# ACTIVITIES

## Chapter 1

*Before you read*

1 Look at the pictures of Who's Who in Sweet Valley High. Who do you think are the most important people in this story?

2 Look at these words in your dictionary.

*alone   boyfriend   competition   good-looking*
*jealous   king   queen   true   twin*

Which word or words would you put in these sentences

a Two sisters or brothers born at the same time are ......

b In the old days the ..... and ..... were the most important people in the country.

c We can say a person with a nice face is ......

d When your ... talks to another girl, sometimes you feel ......

e Some people do a lot of ..... and win a lot of things.

f He told me he lived in London, but it was not ..... – he really lived in the country.

g My father died last year and now my mother lives ......

h *Sweet Valley High* is the name of the school in this story. Find out what the words mean.

*After you read*

3 Who says this? Who to?

a 'He's different now and I am, too.'

b 'Smile that beautiful smile for him and I know he'll ask you.'

4 How are Elizabeth and Jessica different?

5 Why doesn't Jessica like Enid?

6 How does Enid know George?

7 What is the story about Ms Dalton?

8 Why is Jessica jealous of Enid?

9 Where do these things happen?

a Enid shows Elizabeth the letters from George.

b Winston asks Jessica to walk with him to the next lesson.

## Chapters 2–3

*Before you read*

10  Find these words in your dictionary

   *heart   kiss   vote   worried*

   a  How do people usually vote

   b  What do you think the students could be worried about?

   c  Make a sentence with the words *kiss* and *heart* in it.

11  What do you think will happen to the letter under Elizabeth's bed?

12  Do you think Winston will ask Jessica to go the dance with him?

*After you read*

13  Who says this? Who to?

   a  'Everybody will be there – everybody important.'

   b  'You can forget Bruce. He's not coming tonight.'

14  Jessica finds George's letter in Elizabeth's room. But why does she go in there?

15  What does Elizabeth think is wrong with Ronnie the night at the cinema?

16  Who is having a party?

17  Why is Lila jealous of Ms Dalton?

18  Who is Bruce going to take to the dance?

19  How do the Sweet Valley High students know about Ronnie, Enid and Elizabeth?

20  Where does Jessica talk to Enid about Elizabeth?

21  Why does Jessica tell Elizabeth she is going to the dance with Ronnie?

## Chapters 4–5

*Before you read*

22  What do you think Elizabeth will do next? Who can help her?

23  Will Enid go to the dance? Do you think she will go with Ronnie or a different boy?

24  Who do you think the dance king and queen will be?

*After you read*

**25** Who says this? Who to?

 **a** 'Now, we must start being detectives.'

 **b** 'How about a kiss for the photo?'

**26** How does Elizabeth find George's letter in her bedroom?

**27** What does Nora Dalton tell Enid *not* to do?

**28** Why isn't Nora going to the dance?

**29** Elizabeth and Lila aren't friends. Why does Elizabeth talk to her at the start of the dance?

**30** Why isn't Ken at the dance?

**31** Why do Jessica's friends vote for Winston?

**32** Where do these things happen?

 **a** Elizabeth talks to Mr Collins.

 **b** Enid talks to Ms Dalton.

 **c** George and Enid meet again after two years.

**Writing**

**33** Write about the autumn dance for the Sweet Valley High school newspaper.

**34** Write three sentences about Nora Dalton, three sentences about Lila Fowler and three sentences about one other person in the story.

**35** Write a different ending to the story. Do you think your ending is better?

**36** Who do you like most in this story? Who don't you like? Write about why you do or don't like these people.

Answers for the Activities in this book are published in our free resource packs for teachers, the Penguin Readers Factsheets, or available on a separate sheet. Please write to your local Pearson Education office or to: Marketing Department, Penguin Longman Publishing, 5 Bentinck Street, London W1M 5RN.